THE DAY THE BANANA WENT BAD

First published in 2020 by Scholastic Children's Books
Euston House. 24 Eversholt Street. London NW1 1DB
a division of Scholastic Ltd
www.scholastic.co.uk

London ~ New York ~ Toronto
Sydney ~ Auckland ~ Mexico City
New Delhi ~ Hong Kong

Text copyright © 2020 Michelle Robinson
Illustrations copyright © 2020 Tom Knight
PB ISBN 978 1407 19932 0
C&F PB ISBN 978 0702 30071 4

Printed in China
10 8 6 4 2 1 3 5 7 9

FSC
www.fsc.org
MIX
Paper from
responsible sources
FSC® C008047

FOR DAN AND CATH
MR

FOR TRACEY, DOUG,
PETER AND JOEY
TK

ONE Banana, TWO banana, three banana, FOUR.

Dumped inside the 'REJECT' bin inside a superstore.

Bad Banana's peeling, feeling hurt and hopping mad.

SALE!

TO CLEAR

"You dare call ME A REJECT?! I'll soon show you all who's BAD . . . "

His fruity friends agree with him.

Banana grabs
a trolley, shouting,

"We're at our BEST just as we are – be PROUD of ALL your bruises!"

They RIP OFF all their stickers, each fruit doing as it chooses.

Banana's trolley soon fills up
with quirky looking chums:

a slightly **SOUR**
satsuma

and an **UNRIPE**
pack of plums.

Odd oranges, old apples,
mushy pears and grapes galore,
all flock to join Banana
as he STOMPS around the store.

LOCK UP all your lemons
and BEWARE your orange juice!
The rotten fruit's REVOLTING . . .

BAD BANANA'S ON THE LOOSE!

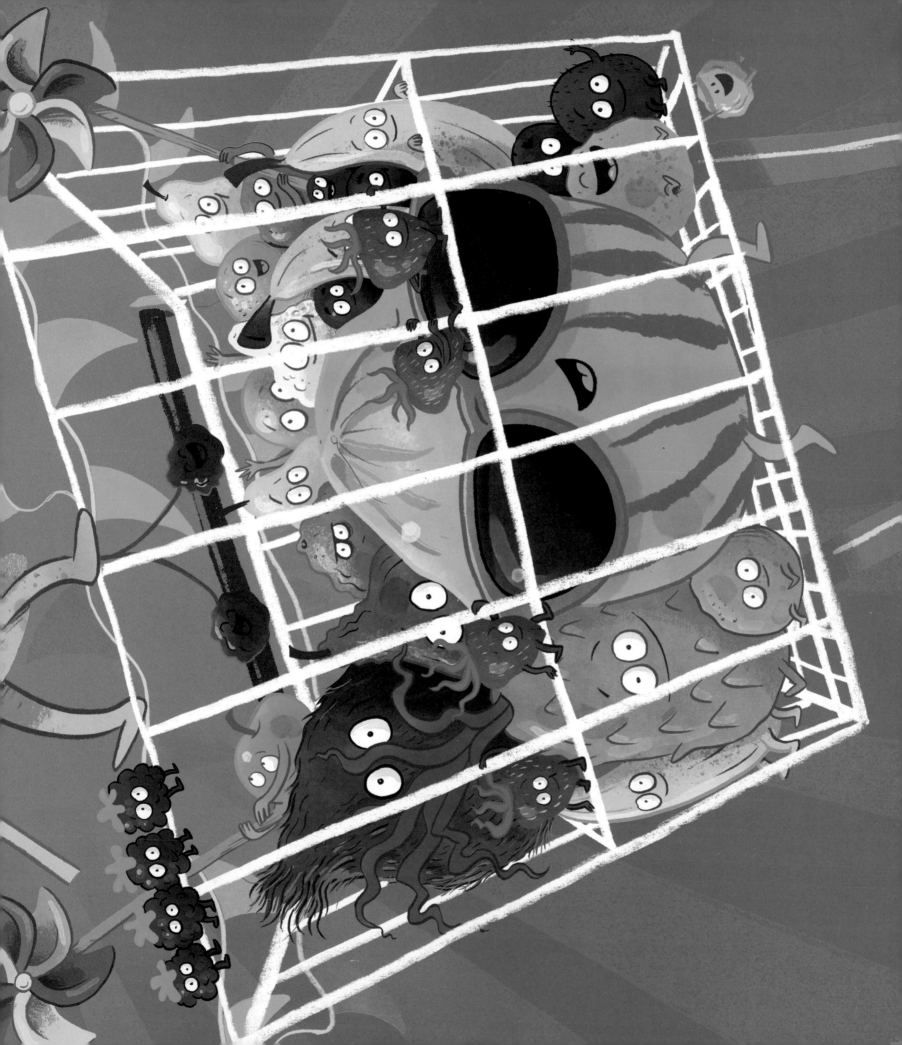

Bad Banana freezes.

cries a grape.

a voice says.
Will this scupper
their escape . . . ?

BEWARE!
The next bit's rude.
D'you know what
Bad Banana did?

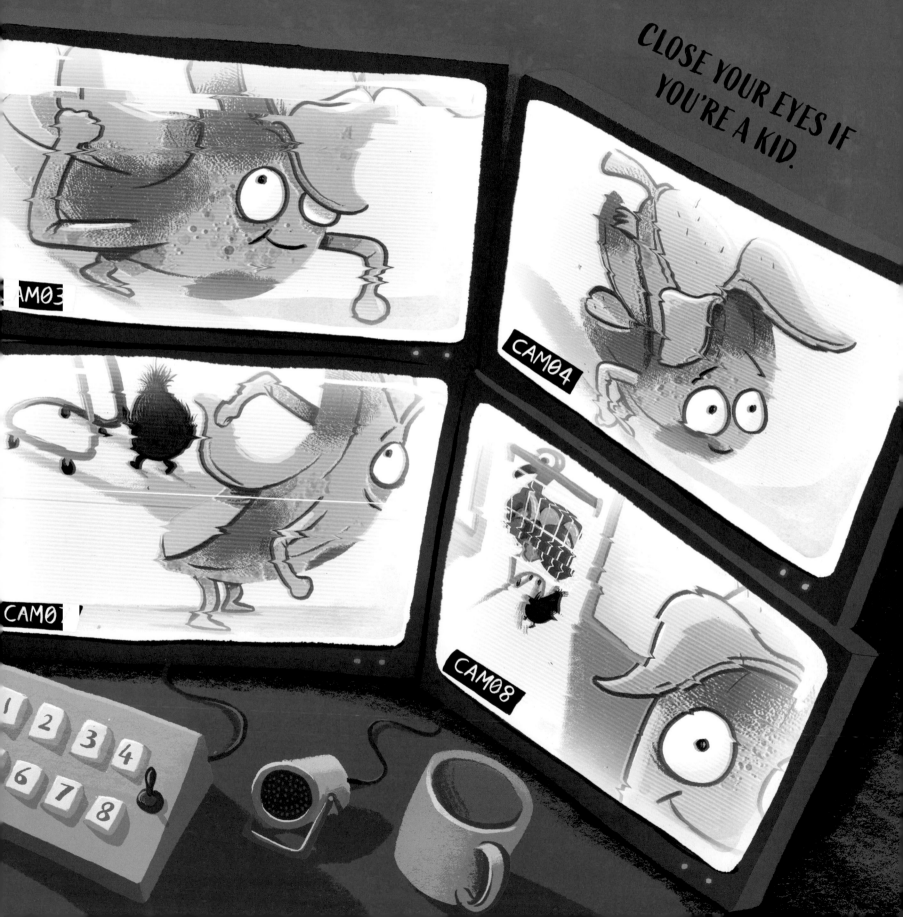

So if you see a trolley where it's not supposed to be,

EXIT

COMPOST 3 FOR £10

It's from the day the
fruit went bad,
but now . . .

. . . they're good and free!
Living their best lives
on some delightful sandy shore,
Bad Banana and his friends . . .

...A LONG WAY FROM THE STORE!

SUMMER SALE